PAPERBACK **PLUS**

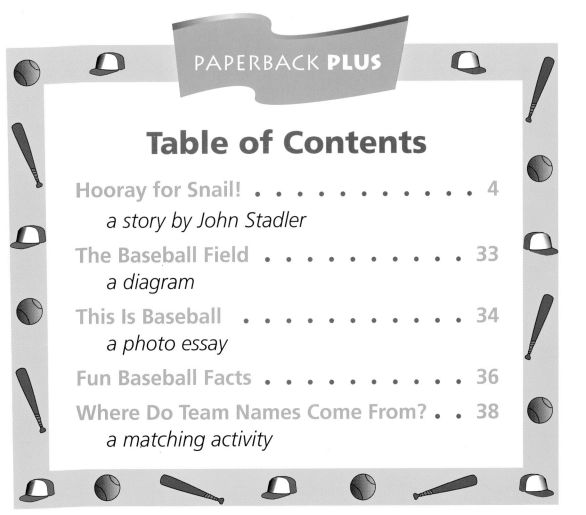

Table of Contents

Meet
John Stadler

John Stadler, Age 7

As a child, John Stadler played baseball all the time. He loved it. That is why he wrote this story about baseball.

John Stadler signing his books

Hooray for Snail!
John Stadler

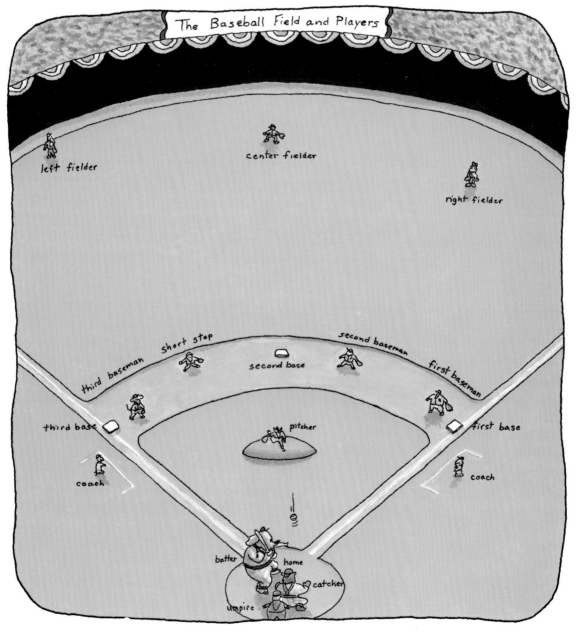

The Baseball Field and Players

left fielder

center fielder

right fielder

short stop

third baseman

second baseman

second base

first baseman

third base

pitcher

first base

coach

coach

batter

home

catcher

umpire

HOUGHTON MIFFLIN COMPANY
BOSTON
ATLANTA   DALLAS   GENEVA, ILLINOIS   PALO ALTO   PRINCETON

Acknowledgments

Grateful acknowledgment is made for use of the following material:

Text

1 *Hooray For Snail!,* by John Stadler. Copyright © 1984 by John Stadler. Reprinted by permission of HarperCollins Publishers.

Photography

ii Courtesy of John Stadler (t, b). **33** Alex S. MacLean/Landslides. **34** Mary Wolf/Tony Stone Images (l); Tim Davis/Photo Researchers (r). **35** Andy Sacks/Tony Stone Images (tl); Paul Barton/The Stock Market (tr); Michael Krasowitz/FPG International (b). **38** New Era Caps Company(tl, tc, tr); Darrell Jones/Tony Stone Images (c); R. Armstrong/Photo Researchers (bl); Karl & Steve Maslowski/Photo Researchers (br).

Printed in Mexico   ISBN 0-395-73214-X   89-HC-98 97

To my teammates:

Bob Wesler
Rick Rennert
James Kanter
Bruce Longstreet

Snail is on the bench.

Snail listens.

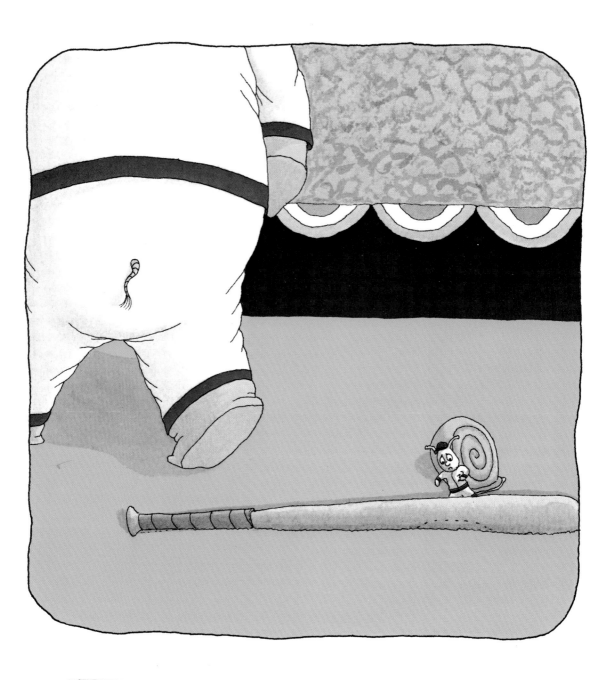

Snail gets the bat.

The bat is heavy.

Snail slams the ball.

The ball flies up.

Snail tips his hat.

The ball goes into space.

Hippo shouts.

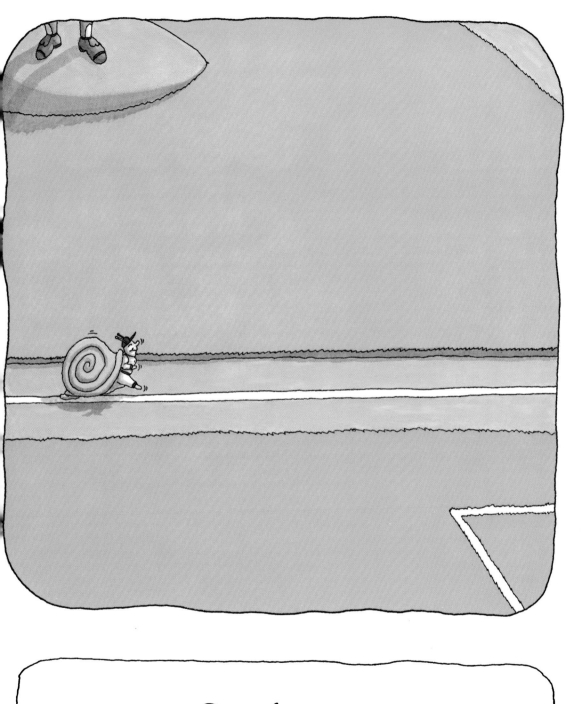

Snail runs.

Snail is slow.

Snail is tired.

The ball hits the moon.

Snail is thirsty.

The ball starts back.

Snail is sleepy.

The ball bounces.

Snail races on.

The ball comes down.

The fielder sees the ball.

Snail runs faster.

The fielder throws the ball.

Here comes Snail.

Here comes the ball.

Snail slides home.

Boom!

Snail is out.

No. Snail is safe.

Snail wins the game.

The Baseball Field

center field

left field

right field

second
base

third
base

pitcher's mound

first
base

home plate

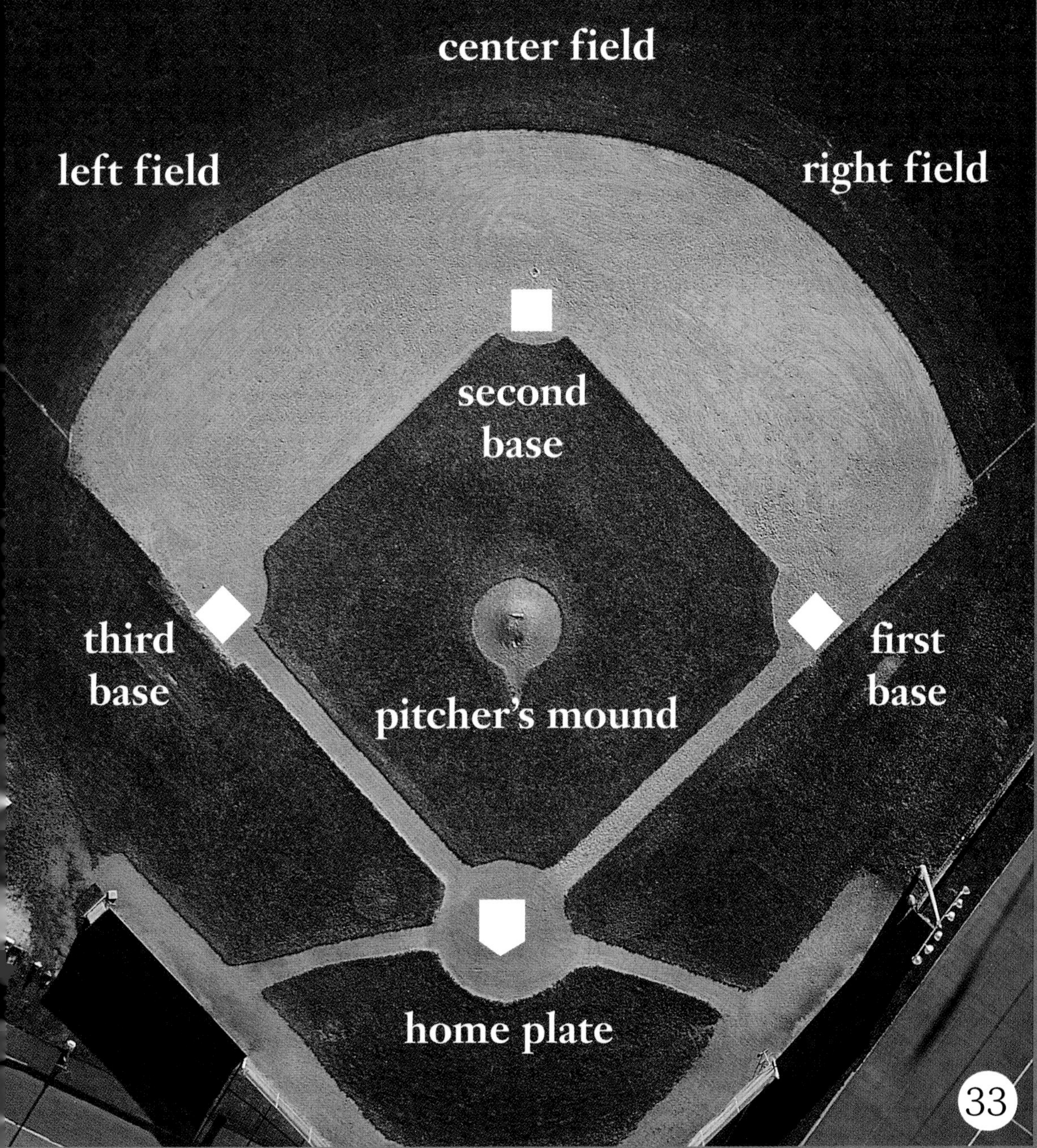

This Is
Baseball

This is a pitch.

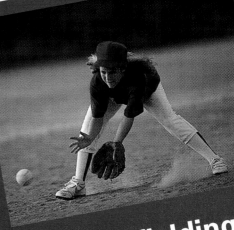

This is fielding.

This is a hit.

This is a catch.

This is a slide.

Fun Baseball Facts

If you like to eat, go to a game in Baltimore! You can get two hot dogs in one bun.

Players on pro teams use only wooden bats.

One hundred or more balls are sometimes used in a pro game.

The longest game was longer than a school day. It lasted eight hours and six minutes.

	BALL 2	STRIKE 1	OUT 1										R	H	E
CHICAGO WHITE SOX	0	1	0	1	3	0	0	0	2	1	1	0	9	13	3
MILWAUKEE BREWERS	0	0	2	0	3	0	1	1	0	0	1	1	9	9	2

Where Do Team Names Come From?

Match each cap with an animal.

A

Toronto Blue Jays

B

Baltimore Orioles

C

Florida Marlins

1

2

3